Mythical Creatures

BERT KITCHEN

LUTTERWORTH PRESS

Cambridge

For
PATRICK HARDY

LUTTERWORTH PRESS,
7 All Saints' Passage,
Cambridge CB2 3LS

British Library Cataloguing in Publication Data
Kitchen, Bert
Mythical creatures.
1. Bestiaries – Juvenile literature
I. Title
398.′.469   GR825
ISBN 0-7188-2646-9

Copyright © Bert Kitchen 1986

First published 1986

INTRODUCTION

I have always been attracted to the image of the Griffin and strange as it may seem, have never really thought of it as an imaginary or mythical creature – it always impressed me as being a completely feasible species. The Griffin inspired me to delve into the world of mythical creatures to see if there existed more such fantastic, yet acceptable combinations.

In my research I found I was continually drawn to those creatures described in classical Greek mythology, but rarely illustrated, and decided to make this the main source of reference for the illustrations in this book. The descriptions of the mythical creatures tend to vary to some degree from author to author, but I have been inclined to use those elements which are most frequently agreed upon to be attributed to each particular creature.

Among the more recognisable creatures such as Cerberus, the three-headed dog, and the half-bull/half-human Minotaur, I have included several less common creatures which attracted me because of their incredible descriptions and the myths that surround them. Some were omitted through lack of space. Others were rejected for differing reasons. The Unicorn, for instance, beautiful creature though he is, belongs to medieval legend. Poseidon, as a tailed merman as he has sometimes been represented, does not fit in with the theme of mythical creatures, as strictly speaking Poseidon was a god, not a creature.

The illustrations are supported by short written passages placing each mythical creature in its setting. They have been kept deliberately short as my aim is to present a visual image difficult to find elsewhere. It is my hope that some people not already familiar with classical mythology will derive pleasure from my illustrations, while others who are will enjoy seeing these creatures, instead of just reading about them.

There are no age limits to classical mythology. Young children are as fascinated by strange creatures and their stories as adults. It is hoped that young and old may find time to ponder and enjoy these fantastic and mythical creatures.

Bert Kitchen.

Bert Kitchen

GRIFFIN

North of the Black Sea, amidst the mountains of Scythia (*Map 1*),
and between the lands of the Hyperboreans and the one-eyed Arimaspians,
lived the Griffins.

Part-eagle, part-lion, the Griffins were the guardians and defenders
of the native gold and other treasures.

Would-be plunderers, like the one-eyed Arimaspians, constantly
harassed the Griffin by attempting to steal the gold; because they made
their attacks on horseback they created a lasting hostility between
the horse and the Griffin.

These confrontations often led to fierce battles but none
of the aggressors could ever match the traditional qualities –
courage, strength and vigilance – of the Griffin or 'lion-eagle'.

HYDRA

A gigantic nine-headed serpent, the terrifying Hydra made its lair
in a marsh close to Lerna in Greece (*Map 2*).

The Hydra's breath was extremely poisonous and it constantly
scoured the countryside destroying crops and annihilating all life in its
path. People in the neighbourhood would tremble with fear
when they knew the Hydra was on the move.

Not surprisingly, no ordinary human being had the courage
to resist it until Heracles, or Hercules, the superhuman hero had, as one
of his twelve labours, the task of tracking down the monster in order
to kill it and end its course of destruction.

In his battle with the Hydra, Heracles found, to his horror, that,
for every head he cut off, two more would grow in its place. With the
help of his assistant, Iolaus, however, he discovered that, by sealing
each neck with burning brands immediately after the head had
been severed, he could stop any regrowth.

Heracles then cut off all the Hydra's heads and, when he finally
reached the immortal ninth one, he took it and buried it under
a massive boulder to ensure that the Hydra would never rise again.

CHIMAERA

In Lycia (*Map 1*) there is a volcanic mountain called Chimaera.
Many fierce lions once lived around its fiery peak, while goats
grazed lower down; at the base there writhed hordes of venomous
serpents. From this mountain emerged the fire-breathing Chimaera,
part lion, part goat and part serpent.

The King of Lycia asked the warrior, Bellerophon, renowned for
his bravery and fearlessness, to seek out and destroy the Chimaera.

Mounted on the winged horse, Pegasus, Bellerophon made an
airborne attack on the earthbound Chimaera, raining down arrows
upon its defenceless head. As the Chimaera gave way to this attack
roaring in pain, Bellerophon flung a wedge of lead into its open
mouth. Under the force of the Chimaera's fiery breath this melted
and flowed, hissing, down its throat, quickly ending the Chimaera's
life in a most horrific fashion.

PYTHON

From ancient records we learn that the Python was a male dragon that emerged from the mud after the earth's primeval floods had receded and when life on earth first began.

Seeking higher ground he made his den in the deep caves of Mount Parnassus in Greece (*Map 2*).

Apollo, god of the sun, youth, poetry and music also looked for a higher place on which to build his temple and accidentally stumbled across the Python's lair. The dragon, upset by this disturbance, sprang at Apollo who, reacting immediately and instinctively, let fly an arrow at the leaping monster. The arrow penetrated the dragon's body between its armoured scales, killing it in mid-flight.

In remembrance of this encounter, Apollo founded the Pythian Games and nearby at Delphi, supposedly the centre of the earth, he built his own temple.

PEGASUS

When Medusa, the serpent-haired Gorgon, was killed by Perseus, Pegasus, the flying horse, was supposed to have appeared from her blood.

The news of the existence of this winged horse soon reached the ears of brave Bellerophon, the Corinthian warrior, who realized that such a mount would be invaluable to him in his encounters on the battlefield.

In order to help him capture the horse, the goddess Athena gave Bellerophon a golden bridle which was known to be endowed with magical power.

One day, descending from the sky at Corinth (*Map 2*) to drink at the well of Pirene, Pegasus caught sight of the golden bridle in the hands of Bellerophon and, under its spell, went quietly to him.

The speed and the flying power of Pegasus proved to be of enormous advantage to the hero in his battles. Later, however, Bellerophon became over-ambitious and attempted to fly all the way to the home of the gods in Olympus (*Map 2*). This upset Zeus, King of the gods, who sent a gad-fly to sting Pegasus and he, in turn, unseated his rider and flew on alone to the stables of Zeus, whose thunder-chariot he has drawn ever since. Following this it is said that Bellerophon, injured by the fall, was left to lead the rest of his life as a blind wanderer.

CENTAUR

The Centaurs, an ancient tribe known for their great strength and ferocity, were originally natives of the mountainous district of Thessaly (*Map 2*), the land of the Lapiths.

When the King of the Lapiths was to be married, as a gesture of goodwill, he invited the Centaurs to take part in the wedding celebrations. At the feast much wine was drunk and the Centaurs, unused to wine, became highly intoxicated. On impulse, one of the Centaurs attempted to carry away the King's bride. This set off a fierce battle between the Lapiths and the Centaurs.

Eventually, the Lapiths emerged victorious and drove the Centaurs out of Thessaly to the borders of Epirus where they were forced to take refuge on the slopes of Mount Pindus (*Map 2*).

Chiron, most famous of the Centaurs, was renowned for his wisdom and knowledge of medicine. Unfortunately, Chiron's life came to a tragic end when he was accidentally and fatally wounded by a poisoned arrow, shot by his friend Heracles. When Chiron died the god Zeus gave him immortality by placing him amongst the stars, renaming him Sagittarius.

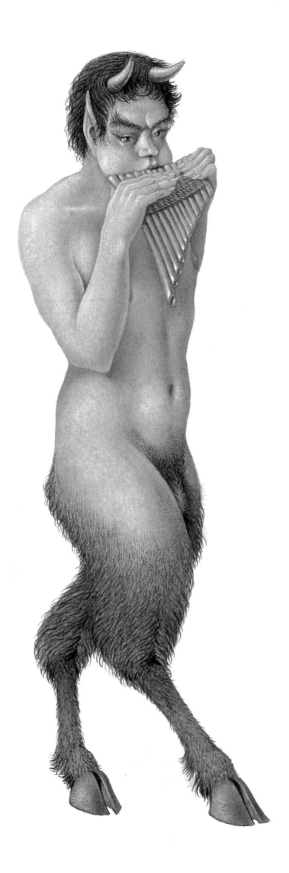

SATYR

Thought to be of Illyrian origin (*Map 2*) the Satyrs, always youthful, personified the spirit of the woodland and countryside both in appearance and behaviour and were also devoted disciples of the god of wine, Dionysus or Bacchus.

Initially they were notorious as a result of their outrageous behaviour at orgiastic parties, their laziness and their persistent pursuit of pleasure. They were often to be seen frolicking in the forest and chasing young maidens.

However, as time went by, their reputation improved as they acquired more civilized manners and became concerned with the pleasures of music and dance.

MINOTAUR

When King Minos of Crete refused to sacrifice the white bull sent
by Poseidon, the sea-god, he took revenge by making Minos' wife
Pasiphae, fall in love with the bull. The result of this union was the
half-bull/half-human Minotaur.

In order to restrain and conceal this monster, Minos had a
labyrinth constructed at Knossos (*Map 2*) on the island of Crete from
which it could not escape and from which no outsider could return
without assistance.

At about this time, King Minos learnt that his son had been killed
in Athens. As a tribute, Minos demanded of the conquered
Athenians that seven youths and seven maidens be sacrificed
to the Minotaur every nine years.

Theseus, son of the King of Athens, vowed to end this
ritual by killing the Minotaur himself, and substituted
himself for one of the seven youths to be sacrificed.

King Minos' daughter, Ariadne, had fallen
in love with Theseus and assisted him in
his task by giving him a sword with
which to slay the Minotaur and a ball
of thread to mark an escape route.

Thus Theseus killed the freakish
Minotaur and escaped from the
labyrinth accordingly.

AMPHITRITE

Amphitrite, Poseidon's Queen, was the leading lady of the oceans
– the principal "Mermaid".

She first came to Poseidon's notice when he saw her dancing with
her sisters on the island of Naxos (*Map 2*) and immediately fell in love
with her.

At first Amphitrite rejected the god's proposals of marriage
and fled into hiding, but the Master of the Seas, having all sea-creatures
at his beck and call, sent a dolphin to find her and bring her back to him.

This the dolphin did, Amphitrite succumbed and became Poseidon's
wife, and the dolphin was rewarded by being set among the stars.

In spite of an apparently harmonious beginning, Amphitrite
had to be patient with her husband's frequent infidelity. Her
patience was tested beyond endurance when Poseidon fell in love
with Scylla.

In her anger Amphitrite scattered magic herbs into Scylla's favourite
bathing pool which transformed her into an ugly monster. This
temporarily regained for Amphitrite her special position in Poseidon's
eyes though, sad to say, this did not last for long as Poseidon was
tempted elsewhere once more.

ECHIDNA

Echidna, a creature who was half-woman, half-serpent, lived in a cave in Libya (*Map 1*) and survived by ensnaring unsuspecting travellers, particularly men, and eating them raw.

Her name is often coupled with Typhon, by whom she bore an incredible array of monsters among which were the Hydra, the Chimaera and Cerberus.

Eventually Argus, the hundred-eyed monster, killed her one evening as she slept.

TYPHON

Typhon was half-man, half-serpent, husband of Echidna and father of her brood of monsters.

His frightening appearance and the war-like cries he uttered struck fear into his adversaries. One day, when he charged into their midst on Olympus (*Map 2*), even the gods fled in terror to Egypt where they disguised themselves as animals to avoid destruction.

Zeus quickly found his true mettle again and returned to Olympus, flinging out thunderbolts and whirling a flint sickle above his head. The sickle struck Typhon, wounding him badly, and he slithered away to Mount Casius, screeching in agony.

Zeus pursued him but Typhon disarmed him using the sickle to sever the sinews of the god's hands and feet. He made it impossible for him to move and abandoned him in a nearby cave.

Friends of Zeus, hearing of his plight, rallied to his aid and, using their magical powers, healed him.

When Zeus regained his original strength he returned once more to Olympus to resume his battle with Typhon, this time mounted on a chariot drawn by six winged horses.

Pelting Typhon with thunderbolts, Zeus gained the upper hand. He wounded the serpent terribly, temporarily paralysing him. Then Zeus crammed Typhon into a crevice at the base of Mount Etna (*Map 1*) and filled the crevice with boulders so burying Typhon alive. Loud grumbles can still be heard coming from this mountain and you can sometimes see sparks flying from the top as Typhon struggles to escape.

GERYON

Geryon reigned over an island called Erytheia which some say lay off the coast of Lusitania, a region of Western Spain.

The island's name, Erytheia, meaning the "red one", probable came from the fact that the island lay to the west, under the rays of the setting sun.

It is no coincidence that Heracles makes an appearance yet again in Geryon's tale. In the tenth of his twelve labours set by Eurystheus, Heracles had to steal Geryon's precious cattle.

Proving his strength and versatility, Heracles first killed the giant herdsman and the two-headed watch dog by strangulation and then proceeded to drive away the precious cattle. Seeing Heracles, Geryon roared from each mouth and gave chase.

Heracles, a master of the art of combat, turned suddenly to face Geryon. Then, running to one side, he fired an arrow which pierced Geryon's three necks, killing him instantly. Heracles took possession of the oxen and delivered them safely to Eurystheus.

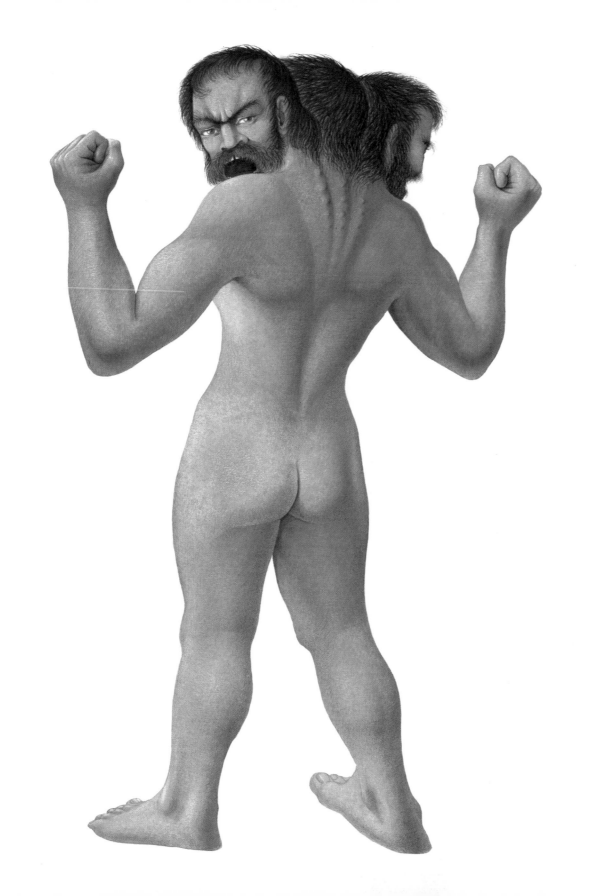

CERBERUS

The three-headed dog, Cerberus, kept guard at the Gates of Hades
to prevent the living from entering. Anyone attempting to pass was
mercilessly torn to shreds. Few men managed to pass Cerberus
and only one of them did so without resorting to trickery of one kind
or another. That man was Heracles.

He had to capture Cerberus as one of his twelve labours without the
use of weapons and to take him to the surface of the earth to show
to Eurystheus, the commander of these tasks.

After overcoming supernatural obstacles on his way through the
underground passages, Heracles finally reached the entrance to Hades.
Taking Cerberus by surprise, he leapt on his back, gripped the dog's
necks in a firm stranglehold and made him semi-conscious. He then
dragged him to the face of the earth and placed him before
Eurystheus.

The task was complete but Eurystheus, out of fear, immediately
released Cerberus. The dog conscientiously scampered back, roaring in
triplicate, to his post at the gates of Hades.

MEDUSA

Medusa was one of the three sisters known as the Gorgons. Snakes grew out of her head and wings from her scaly body. According to some descriptions her face was terrible in beauty and sadness. Anyone who looked at it was turned to stone. Medusa was killed by the hero Perseus. The goddess Athena lent him a shining shield, and using it as a mirror, he crept up while she slept and stabbed her. From her blood sprang the winged horse Pegasus.

FURTHER READING

Larousse Greek and Roman Mythology. Joel Schmidt. McGraw-Hill
    Book Company. English translation 1980.
Larousse Encyclopedia of Mythology. Introduction by Robert Graves.
    Paul Hamlyn 1959.
The Oxford Classical Dictionary. Edited by N.G.L. Hammond and
    H.H. Scullard. Oxford University Press 1970.
A Dictionary of Mythologies. Max S. Shapiro and Rhoda
    A. Hendricks. Granada 1981.
Crowell's Handbook of Classical Mythology. Edward Tripp.
    Thomas Y. Crowell Publishers 1970.
The Greek Myths. Robert Graves (two volumes). Penguin 1955.
Myths of Greece and Rome. Thomas Bullfinch. Allen Lane 1979.
A Dictionary of Classical Reference in English Poetry. Eric Smith.
    D.S. Brewer/Barnes & Noble 1984.
A Companion to World Mythology. Richard Barber.
    Kestrel Books 1979.